Table of Contents

Curriculum Overview

Curriculum Expectations covered in this unit:

The student:

- Demonstrates an understanding that Canada is a country of many cultures
- Identifies community celebrations that reflect their heritage and Canadian identity
- Describes family history and traditions made by individuals and groups in the local community

Teacher Tips

What I Think I Know / What I Would Like to Know Activity

A great way to engage children in a new theme is to ask them what they think they know about a subject and what they would like to know about a subject. Complete this activity as a whole group brainstorming session, in cooperative small groups or independently. Once children have had a chance to contemplate the theme, combine all information to create a class chart to display in the classroom. Throughout the study, periodically update the children's progress in accomplishing their goal of what they want to know and validate what they think they know.

Morning Messages

Morning Messages provide students with interesting facts about the theme they are studying. They may also be used to arrange teachable moments in the use of punctuation, if the teacher chooses to re-write the messages making "mistakes" for the student to seek and correct. Morning Messages are an excellent way to get the learning going when the students enter in the morning. There are several Morning Messages included with this unit.

Reading Cloze Activities

Cloze activities are not only useful for learning new information, but are great to practise reading skills. The children practise reading each cloze page individually or with a friend and finally with the teacher. Initial the page if reading is satisfactory.

Word List

Word Lists create a theme related vocabulary. Place word lists on chart paper for students' reference during writing activities. Encourage students to add theme related words. In addition, classify the word list into the categories of nouns, or verbs and adjectives.

Sample Morning Messages

Did you know Rosh Hashanah is the jewish New Year it is celebrated the first and second days of Tishri. Tishri is the seventh month of the Jewish calendar which is usually around September It is a time of Family gatherings, special Meals and sweet tasting Foods. on the tenth day of Tishri is Yom Kippur This is the Day of Atonement. it is the most solemn day of the Jewish year It is a Day of fasting, reflection and prayers

Did you know Passover is the eight-day ceremony remembering the freedom and departure of the Israelites from egypt during the reign of the Pharaoh Ramses II. It is A time of family gatherings and Big meals called Seders The story of Passover is retold through the reading of the Haggadah. passover is Celebrated the 15th night of the Jewish month of Nissan in the Hebrew Calendar, which is usually in April

Did you know Purim is the most festive of Jewish holidays It is a time of prizes, noisemakers, Costumes and treats. the Festival of Purim celebrates a major success over Cruelty and is told in the Megillah, the scroll of the story of Esther

Purim is Celebrated the 14th night of the Jewish month of Adar in the Hebrew Calendar, which is Usually in March

Sample Morning Messages

Did you know the Bill of Rights says that everyone in canada must be treated equally It doesn't matter What race, colour, national origin, Language, religion or sex they are, all people have the same rights. The Bill of Rights is An official document that was brought into power in 1960 Aren't you happy you live in a free country. be proud to be canadian

Did you know on February 15, 1965, at noon, the red and white maple leaf flag was Raised for the very first time in canada. Early in 1964, Prime Minister lester B. pearson asked people to submit ideas for a new Canadian flag. a red flag with a single, red maple leaf on a white square. Was the design chosen. The flag is a symbol of freedom, peace, respect, justice and tolerance

Jean Chrétien, Prime Minister of Canada, declared that February 15 would be celebrated as National Flag of Canada Day. Wave it proudly

Sample Morning Messages

Did you know Divali is an East-Indian festival of light. the celebration last for two to three days. It is the happiest occasion for all Hindus. it represents the Success of the gods over evil. The goddess of Wealth is worshipped for success, and family ties are made stronger through various Customs during the divali days.

Did you know On May 21, 2002, May was declared Asian Heritage Month Asian Heritage Month is a way for all canadians to celebrate the Beauty and wisdom of the many Asian cultures.

Minister sheila copps, the former Secretary of State of Multiculturalism agreed, along with Others members of parliament, to make may the official asian heritage month

Did you know Muslims celebrate the Islamic customs of fasting For a full month during the month of Ramadan, Ramadan is the ninth month of the Muslim calendar. It can be celebrated in November, december, January, or february. the start of the celebration depends on the sighting of the moon. It is during this month that Muslims observe the Fast of Ramadan. muslims fast During the daylight Hours and in the evening eat small Meals and visit with friends and family. It is a time of worship and thought. a time to make family and community ties Stronger

Research Reporting Opportunities

Research is a fun way to teach children how to read informational text and express what they have learned in their own words. It is easy to set up a theme related centre. Set up a special table with theme related information materials including, books, tapes, magazines etc.

When introducing the children to the use of non-fiction books as a source for their research writing discuss the different parts usually found in a non- fiction book:

The Title Page: Here you find the book title and the author's name.

The Table of Contents: Here you find the name of each chapter, what page it start on and where you can find specific information.

The Glossary: Here you find the meaning of special words used in the book.

The Index: Here you find the ABC list of specific topics you can find in the book.

Next, discuss with the students the expectations of what a good research project should include:

1. number of interesting facts;
2. the use of proper grammar and punctuation, for example capitals, periods;
3. the size of print so that it is easy to read from far away;
4. the use of good details in colouring and the drawing of pictures.

Student Self-Assessment Rubric:
Students use the rubric to evaluate themselves and the work they produce.

Calendar:
Use the calendar at the beginning of each section to record special events and celebrations in your classroom.

Holidays & Celebrations

Special Days in Canada

January 1st	New Year's Day
February 14th	St. Valentine's Day
February 15th	National Flag Day
March 17th	St. Patrick's Day
April 1st	April Fool's Day
May 24th	Victoria Day
July1st	Canada Day
September 1st	Labour Day
October (First Monday)	Thanksgiving
October 31st	Halloween
November 1st	All Saints Day
December 25th	Christmas
December 26th	Boxing Day
December 31st	New Year's Eve

Special Days in the Provinces & Territories

Ontario	Civic Holiday [first Monday of August]
Quebec	National Day [June 24]
Nova Scotia	Natal Day [first Monday, August, except in Halifax where it varies from year to year, [usually Aug or July]
New Brunswick	New Brunswick Day [First Monday, Aug]
Manitoba	Civic Holiday [first Monday, Aug]
British Columbia	British Columbia Day [first Monday, Aug}
Prince Edward Island	Natal Day [usually on first Monday of Aug]
Saskatchewan	Civic Holiday [first Monday of Aug]
Alberta	Alberta Family Day [third Monday of Feb] Heritage Day [first Monday of Aug]
Newfoundland	Celebrated on nearest Monday: St. George's Day [Apr. 23] Discovery Day [June 24] Memorial Day [July 1] Orangemen's Day [July 12] Regatta Day / Civic Holiday [fixed by municipal council orders]
Northwest Territories	Civic Holiday [first Monday of Aug]
Yukon	Discovery Day [third Monday of Aug]
Nunavut	Nunavut Day [July 9] Civic Holiday [first Monday in Aug]

Traditions and Heritage

Did you know traditions are customs or the passing down of information from one generation to another? Many of our beliefs or customs come from our grandparents and parents. Our grandparents and parents were taught their beliefs or customs from their grandparents and parents. This is how our heritage is made.

Canada is made up of many different people. These people come from all over the world. Many of the traditions have been passed down in the families of people who came to Canada from other countries.

For example, did you know giving someone the "bumps" on their birthday was a tradition that started in England and Ireland? When the people from England and Ireland came to Canada, they brought the tradition of lifting a child up and bumping them on the floor for good luck!

In Scotland, people put a dab of butter on the nose of the birthday child. This was supposed to make the child too slippery for bad luck to catch. In Atlantic Canada, where many Scottish people settled, the tradition is still carried on!

Thinking about: Traditions and Heritage

Fill in the missing words from the reading. Use the word box to help.

_____ is made up of

_____ many people. These

_____ come from all over the

_____. Many of the traditions have

been passed down in the _____ of

people who came to Canada from other

_____.

Word Box:

Canada	different	people
World	countries	families

Thinking about: Traditions and Heritage

Make a list of the traditions celebrated by your family.

_____

_____

_____

_____

_____

_____

_____

_____

Share your list with your classmates.

1. Are there any traditions that are celebrated by many people in your class?

2. Are there traditions that are celebrated by only your family?

GeoWat innovative teacher publishing ©2003

Canada: Our Heritage

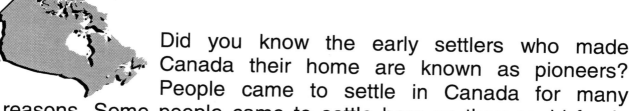

Did you know the early settlers who made Canada their home are known as pioneers? People came to settle in Canada for many reasons. Some people came to settle here so they could freely practise their religion. Some people settled here because they did not like the way their home countries were run. People came to Canada for a better life.

Aboriginal peoples are the only people truly from the country we call Canada. All other Canadians have ancestors who decided to make Canada their home. Some Canadians have ancestors from early pioneer times. Some Canadians have grandparents or parents who moved to Canada. Some Canadians are newly arrived to Canada.

Think about it!

1. What are three reasons early settlers chose to come to live in Canada?

_____

_____

_____

2. Discover what countries your family is originally from and why they chose to make Canada their home.

_____

_____

Canada: Our Heritage

1. Pretend you are moving to another country. What are ten things you would take with you?

2. What kind of feelings do you think an early settler had coming to Canada for a better life? Explain.

_____

_____

_____

3. Survey your classmates and find out where their ancestors are from. Make a list of the countries.

_____

_____

_____

Create A Family Tree

Trace how far back your family tree can go!

Where were you born? _____

What parts of the world is your family from?

_____

_____

_____

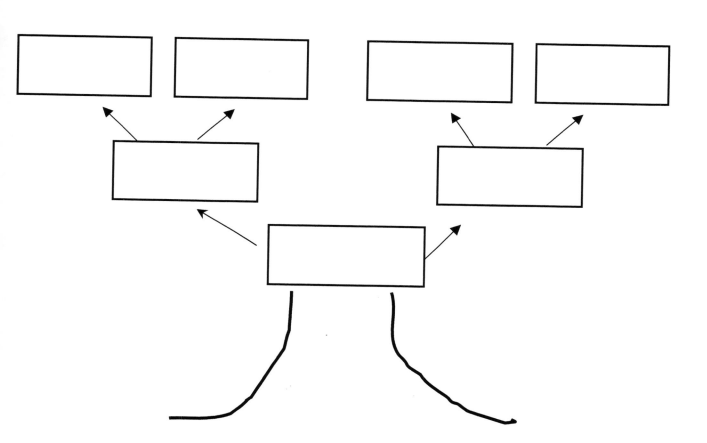

Share your finding with your classmates.

Canada's Symbols

The Maple Leaf

 Did you know when people see a red maple leaf they think of Canada? The maple leaf is on Canadian money that was made between the years 1876 and 1901. Some regiments of Canada's army, use the maple leaf on their badges. The Royal Arms of Canada, the crest Canada uses over the world, has three maple leaves on it.

The Canadian flag has a big red maple leaf in the centre of a white square. On each side of the maple leaf is a band of red. The maple leaf flies proudly over many Canadian buildings and houses.

The Maple Tree:

Did you know the maple tree was made Canada's official symbol on April 26, 1996? The maple tree has played an important part in Canada's history. It is a very good wood to make houses and lumber because it is a hard wood. The maple tree is a very pretty tree changing its leaves in the fall to beautiful colours of red, orange and yellow.

The aboriginal people knew how important the maple tree was in making a sweet treat called maple syrup. They taught the European settlers who came to Canada all about collecting maple sap in the spring and turning it into maple syrup, candy and sweet maple butter!

Today the Canadian maple syrup industry produces some of the best maple syrup in the world!

Canada's Symbols

The Beaver

Did you know the beaver is a symbol of Canada? When early explorers came to Canada, they found hundreds and hundreds of beavers! At that time, beaver pelts or skins were made into hats and trimmed ladies' coats. The fur became very popular in Europe. Traders came to Canada to hunt beaver and sell the fur. The Hudson Bay Company was formed to buy and sell beaver fur along with other goods. Today we know the Hudson Bay Company as "The Bay".

The Moose

Did you know the moose is a Canadian symbol? Moose are found everywhere in Canadian forests, and their picture can be found on the back of a quarter. The moose is an herbivore and it loves to nibble juicy leaves, twigs and plants. The moose loves to swim. Its favourite treat is water lilies!
A bull or male moose can weigh as much as six wrestlers, and stand taller that most men! That means a kindergarten child would be up to the bull moose's knee! Only bull moose have antlers. Females, or cows are smaller than bulls but they still can be as big as a large horse!

Other Canadian symbols:

There are other things that make people think of Canada, when they see them. For instance, the Bluenose II is a ship on the back of the Canadian dime. The Royal Canadian Mounted Police or RCMP represents Canada. Research to find other symbols at:

www.craigmarlatt.com/craig/canada/symbols_facts&lists/symbols.html

Canada's Symbols Word Search

B	D	F	G	H	J	K	L	P	I	Y	T	R	W	C
Q	E	R	T	Y	U	I	O	A	D	F	H	J	K	A
L	M	A	P	L	E	S	Y	R	U	P	K	C	V	N
B	N	M	V	A	D	X	R	T	G	B	H	J	K	A
D	F	C	G	E	H	J	B	V	C	X	D	E	W	D
K	I	J	B	G	R	C	M	P	T	R	F	V	C	A
F	L	A	G	W	D	C	V	G	F	J	Y	R	E	G
A	M	H	F	S	E	S	O	N	E	U	L	B	D	O
E	L	O	I	U	Y	H	G	L	R	A	D	E	W	O
L	Q	S	C	D	E	R	P	Y	U	D	K	L	O	S
E	B	X	N	M	O	O	S	E	N	A	M	J	U	E
L	N	J	K	I	Y	F	G	R	E	N	D	F	R	Y
P	L	I	U	G	R	C	B	H	M	A	N	H	G	F
A	V	F	R	L	K	H	G	D	S	C	C	F	O	T
M	H	G	F	D	S	A	W	R	T	O	Y	U	K	J

BEAVER

MOOSE

RCMP

MAPLE SYRUP

MAPLE LEAF

CANADA GOOSE

O CANADA

BLUENOSE

FLAG

GeoWat innovative teacher publishing ©2003

The National Anthem of Canada
O Canada!

Did you know Canada's National Anthem was composed for the French-Canadian National Festival? In early 1880, Calixa Lavallée was asked to make a song for the festival that was supposed to be for French-Canadians. Lavallée wrote the music while Adolphe-Basil Routier wrote the French words.

In 1901 O Canada was performed in English in Toronto, and became popular all over Canada. There were many English versions made of the song, but Mr. Justice Robert Stanley Weir wrote the English version that we use now.

The song did not become the official National Anthem until July 1st, 1980.

The words of the song that say: "True patriot love" mean that Canadian will be true to their country. "With glowing hearts" means with pride in our hearts, "we see thee rise" means we see Canada prosper. "The True North strong and free" speaks about how Canada is a country that is free where people can say things without fear. It tells about how Canada is a northern country that stands strong against any enemies. "We stand on guard for thee" means we will protect Canada.

When the National Anthem is played it is respectful to stand straight and tall to show how you are proud to be Canadian!

O Canada

O Canada!
Our home and native land!
True patriot love in all thy sons command.
With glowing hearts we see thee rise,
Our true North strong and free
From far and wide, O Canada,
We stand on guard for thee.
God keep our land glorious and free!
O Canada, we stand on guard for thee.
O Canada, we stand on guard for thee.

O Canada!
Where pines and maples grow,
Great prairies spread
And lordly rivers flow,
How dear to us thy broad domain,
From East to Western Sea,
Thou land of hope, for all who toil!
Thou True North strong and free!
God keep our land
Glorious and free!
O Canada! We stand on guard for thee!
O Canada! We stand on guard for thee!

O Canada!
Beneath thy shining skies
May stalwart sons
And gentle maidens rise,
To keep thee steadfast through the years
From East to Western Sea,
Our own beloved native land!
Our True North strong and free!
God keep our land,
Glorious and free!
O Canada! We stand on guard for thee!
O Canada! We stand on guard for thee!

Ruler Supreme, who hearest humble prayer,
Hold our Dominion in Thy loving care.
Help us to find, O God, in Thee
A lasting, rich reward,
As waiting for the Better Day
We ever stand on guard.
O Canada! We stand on guard for thee!
O Canada! We stand on guard for thee!

Ô Canada!
Terre de nos aïeux,
Ton front est ceint de fleurons glorieux!
Car ton bras sait porter l'épée,
Il sait porter la croix!
Ton histoire est une épopée
Des plus brillants exploits.
Et ta valeur, de foi trempée,
Protégera nos foyers et nos droits,
Protégera nos foyers et nos droits.

Sous l'oeil de Dieu, près du fleuve géant,
Le Canadien grandit en espérant.
Il est né d'une race fièrce,
Beni fut son berceau.
Le ciel a marqué sa carrière
Dans ce monde nouveau.
Toujours guidé par sa lumière,
Il gardera l'honneur de son drappeau,
Il gardera l'honneur de son drapeau.

De son patron, précurseur du vrai Dieu,
Il porte au front l'auréole de feu.
Ennemi de la tyrannie
Main plein de loyauté,
Il veut garder dans l'harmonie
Sa fière liberté;
Et par l'effort de son genie,
Sur notre sol asseoir la vérité,
Sur notre sol asseoir la vérité.

Amour sacré du trône et de l'autel,
Remplis nos coeurs de ton souffle immortel!
Parmi les races étrangères,
Notre guide est la loi:
Sachons être un peuple de frères,
Sous le joug de la foi.
Et répétons, comme nos pères,
La cri vainqueur: "Pour le Christ et le roi,"
La cri vainqueur: "Pour le Christ et le roi,"

January 200___

New Year's Day

Did you know most Canadians celebrate the arrival of the New Year with a big party? The celebration of New Years is one of the oldest traditions. It can be traced back in time to ancient Babylon about 4000 years ago. Back then New Years was celebrated on the first day of spring. It symbolized the beginning of a new season.

January first has been celebrated as New Years for about 400 years. Tradition has it that people make a "New Year's resolution". That means that you promise to change something in your life for that year. For instance many adults promise that they will go on a diet for the year, or change their exercise habits. Sometimes New Year's resolutions are broken before the end of January!

 A symbol of the New Year is often a small baby. The new baby signals the beginning of a new time, while the ending year is often an old man.

It was believed that the people you spent the first day of the New Year with and what you ate on that day could affect your luck. So the tradition of New Year's parties began. People surrounded themselves with good friends to bring good luck in the New Year.

It is also a tradition to sing a song called "Auld Lang Syne". This song is sung at midnight and means "the good old days".

Thinking about: New Year's Day

Think about what you would like to change in this New Year. Make a resolution, or promise to make that change. Write your resolution here:

_____

_____

_____

_____

_____

"Le Carnaval de Quebec"

Did you know the Quebec Winter Carnival is the largest winter carnival in the world? It began in 1894 when people were tired of the long hard winter in snowy Quebec City. They decided to get together just before Lent (the 40 days before Easter) to have a big party. This happened around the end of January and the beginning of February.

"Bonhomme Carnaval" is the mascot for the carnival. He is a huge snowman who wears a "ceinture flechee" and a toque. A "ceinture flechee" is a woven belt that was worn by early Quebec fur traders. A toque is a woolen hat usually with a pom-pom at the end!

For seventeen days, the Quebec Winter Carnival celebrates winter by offering night parades, snow baths, snow sculpture competitions, canoe races over the frozen St. Lawrence River, soapbox derbies, dog sled races and huge slides from the upper city to the lower city.

A queen is crowned and she and Bonhomme rule the city. A parade through the centre of town is the highlight of the festivities. "Carnaval" celebrates the old customs of Quebec. In those days canoeing across a frozen river or dogsledding was a way of transportation for the people who lived in Quebec.

Nearly a million people visit "Le Carnaval de Quebec" every year!

Thinking about: "Le Carnaval de Quebec"

Fill in the missing words from the reading. Use the word box to help.

Did you know the _____ Winter Carnival is the

_____ winter _____ in

the _____? It began in 1894

when _____ were _____ of

the long hard _____ in

_____ Quebec City.

Word Box:

world	Quebec	winter
largest	snowy	carnival
tired	people	

Using the information from the reading, write about the kinds of things you want to see or do at, "Le Carnaval de Quebec". Explain your thinking.

_____

_____

_____

February 200___

Valentine's Day

Did you know the first paper valentine was made in the 1500's? In the early Roman times, there was a great festival every February. Young women would place their name in a box. A young man would draw a name from this box and this was supposed to be his love.

Valentine's Day is time that has been set aside to honour love. Every February 14th, people celebrate this romantic tradition.

There are many symbols that make people think of Valentine's Day. **Cupid** is a child with wings whose magic arrows pierce the hearts of his victims. This causes them to fall deeply in love!

Hearts are often linked to feelings of love. Long ago people believed all feelings came from the heart. Later they thought only love came from the heart, and it became the symbol for love at Valentine's Day! Today, candy is often packaged in heart-shaped boxes.

Red Roses were supposed to be the favourite flower. Red is the symbol for strong feelings. This is why the red rose was chosen as the flower for Valentine's Day.

Doves and Lovebirds are often found on Valentine's Day cards. Lovebirds are beautiful parrots that sit closely together in a pair. People thought this symbolized love. Doves were supposed to be the favourite bird of Venus, the Goddess of Love. Doves stay with the same mate for all their lives. Both the male and the female birds care for the young. These birds stand for loyalty and love, so they made a perfect symbol for Valentine's Day.

Thinking about: Valentine's Day

Fill in the missing words from the story. Use the word box to help.

There are many _____that make

_____think of Valentine's Day.

_____is a child with _____whose

magic_____pierce the

_____of his_____.

This causes them to fall _____ in

_____!

Word Box:

Cupid	hearts	deeply
arrows	symbols	people
wings	victims	love

St. Valentine's Day

S	M	P	G	Y	W	O	Q	S	R	E	W	O	L	P
R	J	L	N	O	D	T	R	A	E	H	S	B	F	K
E	Z	H	P	Y	D	W	E	R	D	T	Y	H	V	S
W	P	L	M	F	I	D	K	R	H	B	D	O	E	T
O	M	J	K	G	H	T	E	O	Q	C	U	P	I	D
L	A	D	A	R	R	O	W	S	H	J	L	M	N	V
F	U	H	G	N	J	G	M	E	S	L	E	G	I	S
B	J	S	L	O	B	M	Y	S	G	N	C	H	Y	D
S	Z	E	X	C	V	B	N	M	I	L	K	J	H	R
P	O	V	E	N	U	S	I	T	U	Y	R	E	W	I
T	I	O	P	Q	W	E	N	R	T	T	Y	U	I	B
P	E	D	A	S	F	E	D	G	H	J	D	M	C	E
A	V	F	G	H	L	J	K	L	V	B	N	G	H	V
J	O	H	R	A	E	T	G	Q	W	E	A	T	Y	O
M	L	B	V	C	X	Z	S	D	F	G	C	J	K	L

ARROWS	CANDY	CUPID
DOVES	FLOWERS	GODDESS
HEART	LOVE	LOVEBIRDS
RED	ROSES	SYMBOLS
VALENTINE	VENUS	

I Love You!

This activity repeats a pattern of hearts, using contrasting colours.

MATERIALS:
- Construction paper in white, red or pink
- Scissors and glue

WHAT TO DO:
1. Demonstrate for the children how to stack two pieces of construction paper on top of each other;
2. Fold the stacked paper in half, lengthwise;
3. Cut heart shapes along the fold;
4. Cut out the heart shapes again leaving a small border along the cut out space;
5. Fold the final piece of construction paper into 4 lengthwise;
6. Glue the cut out shapes vertically in each of the panels on the final piece of construction paper.

TEACHER TIP:
Use simple seasonal shapes such as pumpkins, shamrocks or Christmas bells for repeat patterns at other times of the year!

Groundhog Day

Did you know groundhogs can predict the weather? On February 2nd, Canadians watch for groundhogs to come out of their den. If the groundhog stays out of its den, then there will be six more weeks of winter. If he sees his shadow and runs back to bed, spring is "just around the corner!"

For centuries in Europe, people brought their candles to church to have them blessed. They called this special day "Candlemas", and it was held on February 2nd. February 2nd is the mid point between winter and spring. An old Scottish poem said, "If Candlemas Day is bright and clear, there'll be two winters in one year".

By the 1840's the idea of predicting the length of winter was left up to the little groundhog. February 2nd was a good date to make the prediction, since this day was half way to spring. If the groundhog saw his shadow, "then Candlemas is bright and clear" and people believed that winter was still not over. They had a long wait until spring.

In Pennsylvania, the groundhog that predicts the weather is called "Punxsutawney Phil". He lives in a wooded knoll just outside of town and is treated very well!

In Ontario, the groundhog who predicts the weather is called "Wiarton Willy". He has a special burrow where he lives and is taken care of year round. People across Canada come to visit Wiarton on February 2nd to see Willy wake up and come out of his burrow. Willy is an albino groundhog. That means his fur is all white. White groundhogs are rare, so Willy is considered an extra special weather predictor!

Groundhog Popper

This little puppet can be the inspiration for a ground hog play, or just for fun on February 2!

MATERIALS:

- Paper or Styrofoam cups
- Popsicle sticks
- Scissors
- Glue
- Markers
- Brown construction paper
- Googly eyes (optional)

WHAT TO DO:

1. Using the brown construction paper, model for the children how to draw a ground hog (use an oval for the body, and a circle for the head. Add details: on the oval to represent the legs and arms and on the circle to represent a snout, etc.)
2. Attach the ground hog to a Popsicle stick;
3. Demonstrate for the children how to decorate the cup and make a small slit on the bottom of the cup, large enough to slip the Popsicle stick through;
4. Insert the ground hog into the cups and make him "pop" by pushing the stick out of the cup.

Predict:
Do you think the groundhog will see his shadow? Why? Explain your thinking.

_____

_____

_____

March 200___

St. Patrick's Day

Did you know St. Patrick is the Patron Saint of Ireland? Tradition says that St. Patrick drove all the snakes out of Ireland. In truth, there were no snakes in Ireland.

St. Patrick was born in Rome around 390ad. He moved to England with his family and was sold into slavery after Irish warriors raided his village. St. Patrick ran away from his owners and took a ship to France. Here he studied to become a priest. Until this time his name had been Succat Maewyn. He changed it to Patrick Magonus Sucatus when he was ordained.

He was sent to Ireland as a missionary to convert the people there to Christianity. The Druids laughed at him, but St. Patrick didn't give up. He continued to talk to the people of Ireland and many began to understand his beliefs.

On March 17th, 461ad, he died. By this time many of the people in Ireland believed in his teachings. Today we celebrate St. Patrick's Day on March 17th. People use shamrocks, leprechauns and the colour green as symbols of this spring tradition.

There is an old Irish belief that if you catch a leprechaun or follow him to the end of the rainbow, you will find his pot of gold!

This is a famous St. Patrick's Day blessing:

"May the road rise to meet you
May the wind be always at your back
May the sunshine warm upon your face
And may God hold you in the palm of his hand"

Thinking about: St. Patrick's Day

Fill in the missing words from the story. Use the word box for help.

"May the _____ rise to meet you,

May the _____ be always at

your _____,

May the _____ warm upon

your _____,

And may God _____ you in

the_____ of his _____"

Word Box:

back	wind	road	sunshine
hold	palm	hand	face

St. Patrick's Day Word Search

L	V	K	I	H	T	N	E	E	T	N	E	V	E	S
O	E	G	H	M	F	G	H	U	T	E	W	C	A	X
Q	R	P	F	D	L	K	L	W	O	B	N	I	A	R
T	Y	I	R	I	S	H	U	I	O	P	A	D	F	G
L	K	J	H	E	G	F	D	S	A	Z	X	V	N	M
M	N	B	V	X	C	N	E	E	R	G	Q	W	R	T
I	Y	U	I	O	P	H	L	K	J	O	H	G	F	V
S	A	D	R	P	H	J	A	K	Y	L	U	C	K	K
S	Y	M	B	O	L	S	M	U	O	D	J	K	J	C
I	V	G	U	T	N	J	I	V	N	D	F	H	U	O
O	W	E	T	Y	U	I	O	A	P	L	K	J	H	R
N	M	N	B	V	C	X	L	P	O	I	J	H	F	M
A	F	G	H	J	I	E	R	T	Y	N	J	I	H	A
R	J	K	H	C	R	A	M	M	N	B	V	C	X	H
Y	C	F	T	I	V	B	N	J	U	Y	T	R	D	S

GOLD	GREEN	IRELAND
IRISH	LEPRECHAUN	LUCK
MARCH	MISSIONARY	POT
RAINBOW	SEVENTEENTH	SHAMROCK
SYMBOLS		

April 200___

Easter and Earth Day Activities

Easter Eggs

Have children cut big oval shapes from construction paper. On the oval shape using water-based markers, instruct children to create interesting line patterns (e.g., jagged, wavy, thick and thin.) Trace over the water based marker with white glue to produce a puffy effect.

Eggs To Dye For!

Have children carefully draw designs on hard-boiled eggs using a crayon. Dip the hard-boiled eggs into dye baths created with food colouring, water and a bit of vinegar. As an alternative to food colouring, use natural vegetable dyes or diluted jelly powder crystals. An alternate way of using eggshells is to crush the shells and immerse them in the dye baths. This will colour the crushed shells, making them a suitable material for mosaic pictures.

Earth Day Sun Catchers

Use the lids from frozen juice cans to create these dazzling sun catchers. Cover the can lid using coloured glue. Swirl the glue together to create a great sea, or create a symbol or replica of the Earth. Allow to dry and peel from the lid. Pierce the glue with a paper clip to hang.

Earth Day Collage

Have children create collages using magazine pictures of animals and natural resources such as water. Once the whole paper is covered, encourage children to find and cut out words or phrases to promote Earth Day awareness. For example, "Stop Pollution" or "The Earth is for everybody".

Easter

Did you know the Easter Bunny was born thousands of years ago? Legends of ancient Egypt told of hares that were a symbol of new birth. Because of these beliefs, the rabbit became linked with spring and the period of renewal of life. Easter eggs were coloured and used during the spring festivals of the Egyptians.

It is thought that eating and giving eggs on Easter came from the time when the church told people they could not eat eggs during Lent, or the forty days before Easter. Giving eggs celebrated the end of Lent.

Easter is a very important celebration for Christians. They believe Jesus Christ rose from the dead on the first Sunday after the spring full moon. Easter usually falls in April, depending on the time of the full moon.

Mardi Gras is the Tuesday before Lent. "Mardi Gras" means "fat Tuesday" in French. It is a time of celebration and parties before having to give up things for Lent. In ancient times people ate fatty rich foods that they were not allowed to eat during Lent.
The day after Mardi Gras is known as Ash Wednesday.

Easter Word Search

E	L	K	J	H	G	F	D	E	T	A	R	T	Y	U
A	A	F	G	H	N	K	L	O	D	S	W	E	R	T
T	Y	S	P	O	U	Y	T	R	E	H	F	D	S	B
S	D	F	T	L	K	J	G	F	D	W	S	D	F	D
P	U	H	L	E	N	T	M	N	B	E	G	G	S	C
Q	Z	X	E	F	R	L	K	J	G	D	F	V	D	E
T	H	N	M	U	E	D	F	R	T	N	B	H	N	S
W	Y	N	N	U	B	B	N	H	U	E	N	N	Y	A
P	I	N	G	F	I	F	T	O	G	S	C	V	B	R
K	L	M	Y	T	R	M	B	C	D	D	E	R	T	G
L	K	J	H	F	T	L	I	R	P	A	G	F	D	I
Q	W	E	R	T	H	Y	U	I	O	Y	O	P	I	D
M	N	B	V	F	R	E	W	S	X	V	G	Y	J	R
O	K	M	Y	A	D	S	E	U	T	T	A	F	H	A
A	S	D	F	G	H	J	K	L	R	T	Y	U	I	M

EASTER	EGGS	MARDI GRAS
BUNNY	ASH WEDNESDAY	REBIRTH
LENT	APRIL	FAT TUESDAY

April Fool's Day

Did you know in the 1500's in France, the New Year started on April first? In 1562 a new calendar introduced New Year's Day as January first. Some people didn't believe the date was changed, so they still celebrated on April first. Tricks were played on these people and they were called "April Fools".

In France, in the springtime, the streams and rivers flowed with newly hatched fish. It was said that any "fool" could catch a fish in the spring! This led to the tradition in Quebec of "Poisson d'Avril" (April fish). Children tape paper fish to the backs of their unsuspecting friends, and yell "Poisson d'Avril" when the friend finds the paper fish!

Today people play practical jokes on each other on April first. If the jokester gets someone to fall for his or her joke, he or she yells "April Fools". The jokes are usually just for fun and the best kind of joke is when everyone laughs and no feelings are hurt.

APRIL FOOL

Thinking about: April Fool's Day

Fill in the missing words from the reading. Use the word box for help.

Today people play _____ jokes on each

other on _____ first. If the _____ gets

someone to fall for his or her joke, he or she yells

" _____ _____ ".

The jokes are usually just for _____ and

the _____ kind of joke is when everyone

laughs and no _____ are

_____.

Word Box:

practical	jokester	April
fun	hurt	April Fools
best	feelings	

April Fool's Day

A	D	S	F	D	L	P	O	I	S	S	I	O	N	K
H	P	I	P	U	Y	T	R	E	W	Q	A	S	F	G
J	K	R	L	K	J	H	G	F	D	S	A	R	P	O
A	S	F	I	G	H	J	B	K	I	M	N	E	B	G
A	P	R	I	L	H	U	K	J	H	G	F	T	F	T
B	R	K	J	H	F	E	E	L	I	N	G	S	G	Y
R	A	G	V	U	N	O	C	F	T	Y	H	E	N	B
C	C	Q	W	S	E	K	O	J	O	N	E	K	L	P
R	T	F	G	P	J	Y	I	L	H	G	C	O	D	E
K	I	L	H	R	V	F	B	E	S	T	W	J	T	Y
O	C	P	F	I	H	G	V	R	T	C	X	E	Z	A
R	A	Y	R	N	F	H	S	I	F	L	U	B	G	Y
S	L	O	Y	G	N	U	F	V	C	X	R	T	P	F
A	S	D	F	H	U	R	T	G	S	C	O	T	F	S
M	O	Y	G	N	I	T	C	E	P	S	U	S	N	U

APRIL	FISH	UNSUSPECTING
FEELINGS	JOKES	FUN
HURT	PRACTICAL	JOKESTER
POISSON	SPRING	APRIL FOOLS
BEST		

May 200___

Victoria Day

Did you know Canadians celebrate the day Queen Victoria was born? The celebration takes place on the nearest Monday to May 24th, the Queen's birthday. When a king or queen rules a country, this form of government is called a monarchy. Citizens in a monarchy do not have a choice as to who will be their leader. Instead, it is their birth that  gives them power. Usually when a king or queen dies, the throne is given to the oldest son. If there is no son, the oldest daughter becomes queen.

Queen Victoria was the head of the British Monarchy, which at the time of her reign, included Canada, Australia, India, New Zealand, and many parts of Africa. Victoria was only 18 when she was crowned queen. Queen Victoria was one of the longest ruling monarchs of the British Empire. She ruled for 64 years and died in her eighties!

On Victoria Day, Canadians usually celebrate with fireworks.

GeoWat innovative teacher publishing ©2003

Victoria Day

Using information from the reading and your own ideas answer the following questions:

1. Why do Canadians celebrate May 24th?

   _____

   _____

2. What is a monarchy?

   _____

   _____

3. How long did Queen Victoria reign?

   _____

   _____

4. How old was she when she started her reign and how old was she when she finished her reign?

   _____

   _____

5. If you were a king or queen, what laws do you think would be important to pass, and why.

   _____

   _____

Victoria Day

V	P	L	M	N	B	S	K	R	O	W	E	R	I	F
S	I	D	F	G	H	J	B	X	C	D	T	U	H	N
Z	D	C	T	N	J	L	J	K	H	V	F	R	S	D
F	R	E	T	A	S	D	C	H	V	G	G	T	F	G
N	B	V	H	O	J	T	E	W	D	Z	A	R	C	H
H	H	F	A	O	R	M	A	M	O	N	A	R	C	H
B	U	R	R	E	W	I	Q	A	H	G	F	E	E	S
F	B	I	R	T	H	D	A	Y	Q	U	E	I	V	I
R	T	B	E	E	V	T	Y	U	I	N	L	G	H	T
R	G	F	A	S	D	F	G	H	J	G	J	N	L	I
G	F	N	E	E	U	Q	P	I	L	I	D	Y	R	R
V	D	N	B	G	R	T	Y	V	F	E	W	E	A	B
B	T	W	E	N	T	Y	F	O	U	R	T	H	N	M
C	C	P	O	I	U	A	O	E	R	T	Y	U	I	O
S	V	A	S	D	F	G	H	J	K	L	Q	W	E	R

Queen   Victoria   Birthday

May   Fireworks   Monarch

Reign   Twenty-fourth British

Mother's Day

Did you know Mother's Day was originally called "Mothering Day"? A long time ago in England, people used to celebrate with mothering cakes a special cake made for moms. This special day was just before Easter and people spent time with their mothers.

Eventually a lady named Julia Ward organized Mother's Day meetings in her town of Boston. Mother's Day didn't really catch on until Anna Jarvis convinced her church to celebrate Mother's Day on the second Sunday of May. This was the day her mother had died, and she wanted to remember her in a special way.

Anna and the people who believed in Mother's Day began to write the government in the United States asking them to make the second Sunday in May 'Mother's Day". It took four years for the first official Mother's Day. In 1914, the president of the United States made it a certified holiday.

Soon Canadians were celebrating their mothers on the same day. Traditionally, children serve their mothers breakfast in bed, or make her gifts. Adults pay tribute to their mothers by buying flowers or candy for their moms. Did you know the carnation is the official Mother's Day flower?

Mother's Day Bouquet

Make a bouquet of carnations for mom!

MATERIALS:

- Assorted tissue paper cut into sheets
- Stapler
- Scissors

WHAT TO DO:

1. Have children lay 3-4 colours of tissue paper flat on top of one another;
2. Model for the children how to fold the tissue paper back and forth as you would when making a paper fan;
3. Have children find the middle of the long strip;
4. Demonstrate for the children how to staple the tissue strip securely;
5. Model for the children how to round the ends of the tissue paper with scissors;
6. Instruct the children to carefully pull apart the "petals" of the flowers, until all colours are separated;

June 200___

Father's Day

Did you know Father's Day is celebrated to honour fathers all over the world? It is not clear how the first Father's Day started, but most people believe it was Sonora Louise Smart Dodd who made it popular.

Sonora Louise Smart Dodd was listening to a speech about Mother's Day. She thought she would like to honour her father in the same way. Her dad raised six children on his own after his wife died. Sonora wanted everyone to know how proud she was of her selfless father.

Sonora wrote to the United States government asking to make Father's Day a national celebration. She asked that every year on the third Sunday in June everyone celebrate their fathers.

In 1916, the president of the United States approved the idea of Father's Day. In 1966, President Lyndon B. Johnson made the celebration a law.

Father's Day is celebrated in Canada as well as many places around the world. Thank you to Sonora Louis Smart Dodd who thought her dad was special!

Thinking about: Father's Day

Fill in the missing words from the story. Use the word box to help.

Sonora _____ Smart Dodd was

_____ to a _____ about

_____ Day when she

_____ she would like to her

_____father in the same way.

Word Box

listening	speech	thought
Mother's	honour	Louise

Father's Day Rock Critters

These little rocky fellows are always a big hit. They may be used as paperweights, or mounted on a piece of wood to make an attractive father's day gift.

MATERIALS:

- Stones
- Tempera paint
- Silicone glue ("Goop" or similar crafting glue)
- Materials to decorate (pipe cleaners, felt, yarn, glitter, beads, etc.)

WHAT TO DO:

1. Clean and dry the stones;
2. Brainstorm with the children possible insects or animals that inspire them when they see the stones;
3. Stack the stones to create the insect or animal;
4. Using the silicone glue, glue the stones in place;
5. Paint the stones, using one colour at a time, allowing them to dry between colours;
6. Using a fine line marker, add details like eyes, mouth, nose, etc.;
7. Use materials to decorate. (hair, ears, tail, etc.)

July 200___

Canada Day

Did you know July 1st 1879 was recognized as a day to celebrate Canada? In 1879, Canada was called the Dominion of Canada. For many years the holiday was called "Dominion Day". On October 27th, 1982 "Dominion Day" was officially changed to "Canada Day". This was because Canada was no longer known as the "Dominion of Canada".

July 1st is a day to celebrate "Confederation". Confederation was the joining together of Canada's provinces, or Canada's birthday! In many places, Canada's birthday is celebrated with fireworks displays, educational, artistic and sports activities.

The Government of Canada usually holds a celebration on Parliament Hill in Ottawa, Ontario. Military bands play and official ceremonies are held to wish Canada a happy birthday. The festival ends with fireworks over Parliament Hill.

Canada Day

D	Q	W	E	G	T	N	E	M	A	I	L	R	A	P
O	D	G	H	U	P	L	J	N	B	F	C	X	Z	W
M	E	R	T	Y	U	I	O	P	L	E	K	P	N	B
I	G	H	L	L	I	H	F	T	Y	S	D	R	F	G
N	A	B	F	G	H	J	K	L	F	T	M	O	H	D
I	F	I	R	E	W	O	R	K	S	I	L	V	K	C
O	N	R	H	K	P	G	R	T	M	V	X	I	S	E
N	C	T	J	S	C	A	N	A	D	A	L	N	G	R
A	S	H	F	H	I	F	R	T	Y	L	J	C	V	E
P	O	D	Y	R	T	N	M	T	S	J	G	E	F	M
Q	W	A	E	R	S	T	Y	U	Y	T	P	S	G	O
L	K	Y	J	H	I	G	F	D	S	Z	R	X	C	N
V	B	N	M	A	T	A	D	F	G	H	J	O	K	I
Q	T	O	P	D	R	H	V	F	R	W	D	J	P	E
F	G	A	V	M	A	C	T	I	V	I	T	I	E	S

ACTIVITIES   ARTISTIC   BIRTHDAY

CANADA   CEREMONIES   DOMINION

FESTIVAL   FIREWORKS   HILL

PARLIAMENT   PARTY   PROVINCES

SPORTS

GeoWat innovative teacher publishing ©2003

Positive and Negative Canadian Windsocks

To celebrate Canada's birthday, proudly wave a Canadian windsock. These simple cut out designs make any one Proud to be Canadian!

MATERIALS:
Red and white construction paper
String or yarn
Aluminum foil paper
Red and white tissue paper

WHAT TO DO:
1. Demonstrate for the children how to fold the red or white construction paper in half;
2. Fold the open end of the paper back to the centre;
3. Trace one side of a maple leaf on the fold;
4. Cut the design through the folds;
5. Lay a piece of aluminum foil paper over the construction paper, and glue in place;
6. Make a cylinder out of the construction and foil paper piece;
7. Punch whole on each side of the cylinder and thread yarn or string through it to hang;
8. Make long "tails" on the windsock out of strips of red and white tissue paper.

Calgary Stampede

Did you know the Calgary Stampede takes place for ten days every year in Calgary Alberta? There are many different rodeo activities. Bareback horse riding, means the rider sits right on the back of the horse. There is no saddle for the rider to hold on to. In saddle bronco riding, the rider has a saddle, but the horse has never had a saddle on its back before. The horse bucks and tosses the rider all over the place! In bull riding the cowboy or cowgirl rides the back of a bucking bull!

There are wild cow milking contests, wild horse races and wild rodeo clowns! In the chuck wagon races, four teams of four horses line up to make a mad dash to the finish line.

As well as all the wild animals, there are blacksmiths competing to see who makes the best horseshoes, and all kinds of activities for everyone to participate in. There is a parade that fills the streets with western music and dancers.

From fireworks at night to fun livestock displays, the Calgary Stampede has something for everyone!

Thinking about: Calgary Stampede

Fill in the missing words from the reading. Use the word box to help.

Did you know the Calgary _____ takes

place for _____ days every _____ in

_____ Alberta? There are

_____ different _____

activities.

Word Box:

ten	Stampede	year
Calgary	rodeo	many

Using the information from the reading, tell what kinds of things you would
want to see or do at the Calgary stampede. Explain your thinking.

_____

_____

_____

_____

_____

August 200___

Note: Holidays in August are generally provincial celebrations. You may wish to refer to the chart of holidays at the beginning of this book.

GeoWat innovative teacher publishing ©2003

September 200___

Labour Day

Did you know the first Monday in September is called Labour Day? Canadians have a holiday on Labour Day every year.

In 1872, it was illegal to be a member of a union. It was on April 15, 1872 that a parade of workers marched in Toronto to demonstrate that they believed Canada should have the right to be members of trade unions. Trade unions are people who work at the same kinds of jobs, and fight to get certain rights for their workers. For instance in 1872, the union wanted the number of hours a person could work to be set at nine hours a day.

There was also a parade in Ottawa in the same year. The workers asked Prime Minister Sir John A. MacDonald to give them the right to form a union. On July 23,1894 the Canadian government passed a law making the first Monday in September a holiday to celebrate working people.

Now every year we usually watch fireworks on Labour Day!

Using information from the reading, answer these questions:

1. Why do we have a holiday on the first Monday in September?

   _____

   _____

2. What is a trade union?

   _____

   _____

3. Do you think Labour Unions are useful or not useful? Discuss your thinking with your class.

October 200___

Thanksgiving

Did you know Canadians invented Thanksgiving? In 1578, Martin Frobisher, a sailor from England celebrated his safe arrival in Newfoundland. He gave thanks for the successful journey. He was later knighted and an inlet in the Atlantic Ocean was named after him. Frobisher Bay is in Northern Canada. Other settlers that arrived after Martin Frobisher continued the custom of celebrating and giving thanks for the things they had.

 The Europeans farmers used to fill a curved goat's horn with fruit and grain to give thanks for the food they had. When these people came to Canada, they kept their tradition. That is how we got the "Cornucopia", or "Horn of Plenty".

French settlers who arrived in Canada with Samuel de Champlain held huge feasts of thanks. They formed "The Order of Good Cheer" and shared their food with the aboriginal peoples.

In 1621, the Pilgrims landed in what is now the United States of America. They celebrated the harvest. Since the United States is farther south than Canada, the harvest time in the U.S. is later, in November. In Canada, we celebrate Thanksgiving the second Monday of October, but it wasn't until January 31st, 1957 that the Canadian Parliament made it an official holiday.

Traditionally Canadians eat turkey with stuffing, cranberries, pies and vegetables. Yummy food for a thankful holiday!

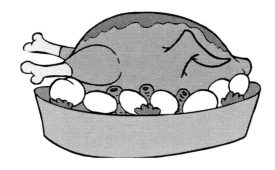

Thanksgiving

F	A	D	F	S	E	I	R	R	E	B	N	A	R	C
R	M	G	N	H	E	N	E	F	B	G	T	Y	O	F
O	H	N	M	A	F	H	W	V	Y	S	M	R	C	N
B	T	I	J	R	C	Y	E	C	G	T	N	N	T	H
I	R	V	U	E	E	R	R	X	N	U	R	M	O	Y
S	E	I	Y	Q	L	D	T	H	C	F	T	J	B	T
H	D	G	T	S	E	C	G	O	B	F	Y	U	E	R
E	X	S	G	C	B	X	P	L	G	I	H	Y	R	F
R	W	K	I	V	R	I	I	I	T	N	U	T	G	V
N	D	N	V	G	A	V	E	D	R	G	J	F	H	C
B	C	A	I	M	T	G	S	A	F	H	M	C	Y	D
V	F	H	D	B	E	Y	U	Y	E	K	R	U	T	W
C	R	T	S	A	E	F	U	D	B	G	H	K	Y	S
X	Y	N	H	D	G	N	J	C	H	D	F	J	H	X
A	B	O	R	I	G	I	N	A	L	C	O	R	N	R

ABORIGINAL   CELEBRATE   CORNUCOPIA

CRANBERRIES   FEAST   FROBISHER

HOLIDAY   OCTOBER   PIES

SHARE   STUFFING   THANKSGIVING

TURKEY   CORN

Corn Harvests

Celebrate Thanksgiving by harvesting Indian corn. This colourful corn can be simulated in this quick and effective activity.

MATERIALS:

- Bristol board
- 3cm. Squares of tissue paper in black, yellow, orange, and brown
- Glue
- Scissors
- Brown paper

WHAT TO DO:

1. Demonstrate for the children how to draw a cob-shape on the Bristol board;
2. Scrunch the pieces of tissue paper into rolls;
3. Glue the wads of tissue paper onto the cob shape;
4. Using the brown paper, create "husks" to attach to the ends of the corn;
5. Decorate the classroom door with the Indian corn cobs!

 **TEACHER TIP:** Recycle paper lunch bags to use as the "husks".

Halloween

Did you know Halloween began a very long time ago? It all started with the druids. Druids were a group of priests from Britain. The druids believed that on October 31st, spirits of the dead, witches and demons wandered the streets. The druids lit bonfires to keep the evil spirits away. They also dressed up in costumes so the evil sprits wouldn't be able to find them. They even thought if they gave the spirits good things to eat, the spirits would be kind to them, and leave them alone.

As time passed, pranks and naughtiness became common on Halloween. People put sod over the chimneys of houses, causing the smoke to back down into the house. People blocked the doors with carts and tapped on windows, startling the people inside. Some boys dressed as girls and girls dressed as boys to fool the neighbours! These tricks were supposed to be the same kinds of tricks the fairies, witches and goblins played.

In Ireland, groups of peasants went door-to-door asking for food and gifts. People who gave "good treats" were supposed to have good luck, while people who did not give treats had "tricks" played upon them. That is why it is the custom to say "trick or treat" on Halloween!

November 1st is the Christian Feast of Hallowmas, or "All Saints Day". The day before was called "All Hallows Eve", which became "Halloween".

The Irish carved faces out of turnips, and candles were placed inside. These turnip lanterns were carried around to scare away evil sprits! When the Irish came to North America, they found pumpkins were more available.

Pasta Skeletons

Making a skeleton out of different shapes of pasta encourages children to know the bones and joints of the human body, as well as having a spooky picture.

MATERIALS:

- Different shaped pasta (bowtie, elbow, spiral, ziti, etc.)
- Black construction paper
- White glue

WHAT TO DO:

1. Brainstorm with the children bones that could be represented by the shaped pasta; (elbow pasta could be fingers, etc.)
2. Demonstrate for the children how to create a skeleton using the different shaped pasta;
3. Explain how they should wait until the skeleton is complete, and they are pleased with their results, before they glue the pieces down;
4. Glue the pasta in place and allow to dry.

VARIATION:
Ask the children how they could place the pasta to make the skeleton appear to be dancing. Explain how changing the placement of the pasta can suggest movement.

Halloween

S	K	N	A	R	P	M	K	L	P	O	L	J	H	B
W	B	M	J	K	U	L	K	J	H	B	M	N	O	M
O	F	J	I	P	M	M	N	A	D	F	A	T	H	L
L	Q	W	E	R	P	T	Y	U	I	U	O	P	I	P
L	H	A	E	R	K	A	D	F	G	O	B	L	I	N
A	N	H	T	E	I	E	D	H	V	H	U	I	O	P
H	Z	X	C	V	N	M	T	F	G	H	J	K	I	Y
U	H	B	G	T	S	I	W	D	F	G	H	Y	R	E
M	H	G	B	V	N	E	E	W	O	L	L	A	H	N
F	R	T	G	E	M	V	S	C	F	T	N	B	V	F
D	V	T	S	U	L	E	V	G	H	U	T	E	W	S
S	C	S	T	K	I	Y	T	E	W	X	C	V	B	T
L	K	S	M	N	H	Y	B	V	D	E	W	B	H	J
D	O	N	N	I	O	R	E	W	Q	X	V	G	T	Y
C	A	N	D	Y	M	J	U	Y	G	D	S	E	W	B

CANDY	COSTUME	EVE
GOBLIN	HALLOWEEN	HALLOWS
NAUGHTINESS	PRANKS	PUMPKINS

November 200___

Remembrance Day

Did you know the 11th hour of the 11th day of the 11th month is a time for silence? This is Remembrance Day. It is a time when we remember all the people who died in the war.

Men and Women from all over Canada fought in World War I. During this war there was a place called Vimy Ridge. Everybody thought the enemy could not be defeated, but the Canadians joined together to win the battle.

During World War II Canadians came together again at a place called Dieppe. This time they were not as successful and many, many Canadians died.

 Today, Canadian soldiers play a very important part in world peace. Soldiers from Canada's armed forces leave their families and go to strange and foreign countries to help the people live in peace.

On Remembrance Day we stand in silence for two minutes. We honour the brave people who helped to keep Canada safe and free. We remember their courage, their sacrifice, and their heroism. We remember that they are someone's dad, mom, sister, brother or sweetheart. We remember we are proud to be Canadian!

Think about it!

On a separate piece of paper, write a letter to an imaginary Canadian soldier to thank them for their hard work and sacrifice.

The Poppy

Did you know poppies are a symbol of remembrance? During World War I, a Canadian Medical Officer named John MacCrae wrote a poem called "In Flanders Fields". John MacCrae was born in Guelph Ontario. In his poem he talks about the red poppies that grow in the fields where the dead soldiers lay.

Poppies had been a symbol of people who were killed in wars for over 110 years. But, it is John MacCrae's poem that describes poppies the best. The poem motivated both the American Legion and the Canadian Legion to make the poppy a symbol to remember the friends and family who died.

It seemed very strange to the soldiers on the battlefield that these beautiful blood-red flowers grew where their friends had died. In truth, the destroyed buildings were made with lime, a chemical found in soil. The rain washed the lime from the buildings back into the soil. The lime is what the poppies needed. The poppies blossomed like magic when the lime returned to the soil. Over the years, as the lime was used up, the poppies began to disappear again.

Thanks to millions of Canadians, the red poppy never dies. Each November 11, it blooms on jackets, dresses and hats all over Canada!

Think about it!

Write your own poem about red poppies.

Poppy Wreaths

Every year on November 11 at eleven o'clock in the morning, Canadians stop and pay tribute to the many Canadian soldiers who sacrificed their lives for our country. The following activity is an excellent way to acquaint children with the sacrifices made by Canadian soldiers, by creating a tissue paper wreath of poppies.

MATERIALS:

- Red and black tissue paper (a large sheet cut in half)
- Scissors
- Stapler or pipe cleaners
- Bristol Board wreath (red is preferred but not necessary)

WHAT TO DO:

1. Have children lay 3 red layers of tissue paper flat on top of one another;
2. Lay one black piece of tissue paper on top of the red pile;
3. Model for the children how to fold the tissue paper back and forth as you would when making a paper fan;
4. Have children find the middle of the long strip;
5. Demonstrate for the children how to staple the tissue strip securely;
6. Model for the children how to round the ends of the tissue paper with scissors;
7. With the black piece in the centre, instruct the children to carefully pull apart the "petals" of the flowers, until all sheets are separated;
8. Attach all the flowers in a large wreath by gluing on the Bristol board circle.

TEACHER TIP:

Have the children use a blackboard compass to make the wreath on Bristol board.
Use this very attractive wreath in a Remembrance Day ceremony.

December 200___

Christmas

Did you know a long, long time ago the Festival of the Ass was celebrated on December 25th? A little girl riding a donkey, or ass would enter the church and all the prayers ended in "hee-haw". In other countries the same date was called the Festival of the Madmen. During this celebration, all the servants became masters and the masters became servants. For that day everything was turned upside down!

 Today Christmas is celebrated in many ways. Santa is an old man in a red coat who drives a sleigh pulled by reindeer. He comes down the chimney to drop presents off to good girls and boys.

In Canada, Christmas is the celebration of the birth of Jesus Christ. Jesus was born in a manger, and in many homes a "crèche" or manger is set up under a Christmas tree.

In Quebec, the night before Christmas is known as "Le Reveillion de Noel". After attending a church mass at midnight, people go home to a huge feast. They eat, drink and celebrate until the early hours of Christmas morning.

Christmas trees are a part of the Christmas season in Canada. Decorated trees can be seen in store, homes and even outside people's houses. Coloured lights, glistening stars and other decorations are placed on the boughs of the tree. Presents are placed under the tree to celebrate the season of giving.

 Carolers sing songs to rejoice and everyone enjoys the magic Christmas brings.

Multicultural Holiday Crafts for December

Hanukkah Stars

Provide children with an outline of a Star of David. Crunch up aluminum foil to crinkle, and unfold to flatten. Cut the aluminum foil in the shape of the Star of David and glue onto blue construction paper. Cut around the shape leaving a border around the star. Colour over the foil with markers, to create a stained glass look.

Kwanzaa Prints

Kwanzaa, Swahili for "first fruit", is a traditional African festival that lasts seven days starting on the twenty-sixth of December. Using green, red, yellow, blue and black paint pads, demonstrate for the children how to use fruit cut into stamps to create various fruit print patterns.

Ramadan Silhouettes

On wet Manila paper, have children create a dawn or dusk effect by applying streaks of yellow, orange and pink paint on the whole paper. Let the paper dry. Meanwhile have children cut out silhouettes of mosques and other buildings found in the community. Paste these silhouettes on the dry dusk or dawn paintings.

Quick Hanukkah Menorah

Make eight balls of clay. Place 4 side by side and add a larger ball. Repeat with the 4 remaining clay balls. With a candle make dents in the clay balls. Dry the clay, and paint to make a Hanukkah menorah.

Gingerbread Dough Decorations

Use cookie cutters and this recipe to create spicy tree decorations or gift tags. 2 cups flour   1 cup salt   2 T ground cinnamon   1 T ground cloves water (about 1 cup) Mix together. Roll, cut and dry. (Dry quickly in a 200°F oven or air dry for several days)

Holiday Wreath

Glue five small pretzels in a circle. Glue five more pretzels overlapping

the first row. Paint with 1 part glue 1 part water to seal. Weave a colourful ribbon through the pretzels.

More Multicultural Crafts

Mexican Huichol Paintings

In the city streets of Mexico, lovely yarn drawings may be found decorating walls, straw items and personal accessories such as purses and wallets. These art pieces are bright and colourful. In this activity children will create yarn paintings, as in the Mexican Huichol yarn paintings.

MATERIALS:
- Pencils
- Construction paper
- Glue
- Scissors
- Yarn (thickest is best)

WHAT TO DO:
1. Demonstrate for the children how to sketch a simple drawing in the middle of the construction paper;
2. Using the glue, spread a bead of glue around the outline of the drawing;
3. Carefully place the a length of yarn into the bead of glue;
4. Fill in the remainder of the picture, spreading glue and laying in the yarn until the whole shape is filled in;
5. Make a border around the picture by laying lengths of yarn around the edges of the picture;
6. Fill in the area between the drawing and the border with strands of yarn in different shapes and colours.

Multicultural Masks

Masks can have important meaning in many cultures. This activity can be used after a discussion of masks around the world, or simply to transport your student to a wild and "other place".

MATERIALS:
- Pencils
- Glue
- String or elastic
- Paint
- Brushes
- Colouring materials, such as markers and crayons
- Scissors
- Bristol board
- Stapler
- Feathers, beads, and found objects

WHAT TO DO:
1. Using a pencil, demonstrate for the children how to make a large oval in the centre of the Bristol board;
2. Cut out the oval;
3. At the top and bottom of the oval, cut a 2-3 cm. Slit;
4. Show the children how to lightly sketch a line though the horizontal and vertical mid-sections of the mask;
5. Demonstrate how to place the eyes and mouth on these lines;
6. Cut the eye and mouth holes out;
7. Decorate the mask with markers, crayons, feathers, beads and other objects that are available;
8. Crossing over the slits at the top and bottom of the mask, stapling in place to create a three dimensional effect;
9. Attach string or elastic to the back of the mask so that it may be attached around the head.

More Multicultural Crafts

Paper-mache Pinata

As part of a multicultural celebration, include a piñata! A piñata is a large paper-mache sculpture or animal usually stuffed with toys, confetti or candy. If you choose to stuff the piñata with candy, please use candy that is wrapped, as unwrapped candy can become sticky and unpleasant. The shape and placement of the balloon will determine the animal or sculpture. In this project the sample is a pig.

MATERIALS:

- Candy, toys, or confetti to stuff the piñata

- 1 large balloon
- 1 small balloon
- 2 paper tubes
- Masking tape
- Paint
- Pipe cleaner
- Construction paper & sparkles (optional)

- Newspaper
- Newsprint
- Cardboard or heavy paper
- Wallpaper paste
- Water
- Paintbrushes
- Scissors

WHAT TO DO:

1. Blow up the balloons;
2. Attach the balloons together using the masking tape. The large balloon will be the body and the small balloon will be the head. Leave the knotted end of the large balloon at the end of the body, to make attaching the tail easier;
3. Cut the two paper tubes in half;
4. Attach the tubes with masking tape to make the legs;
5. Stuff the legs with newspaper; (This will keep the candy in the body once the balloons are popped)
6. Out of the cardboard or heavy paper, shape two ears;
7. Attach to the head with masking tape;
8. To the knotted end of the large balloon, attach a pipe cleaner;
9. Secure the pipe cleaner with masking tape;
10. Mix the wallpaper paste with water until it is the consistency of heavy cream;
11. Rip the newspaper into strips;
12. Dip the strips of newspaper into the wallpaper paste mixture
13. Hold the strips between your pointer and middle fingers and pull though to remove excess paste;
14. Cover the balloons with the paste-covered strips until there are four layers of newspaper;
15. Add a layer of unprinted newsprint; (This will facilitate painting, keeping the newspaper ink from bleeding through)
16. Allow to dry for several days;
17. Cut a small flap in the top of the piñata when completely dry;
18. Pop the balloons;
19. Make two small holes in the piñata at a point where it will hang properly and add string;
20. Add "goodies" such as wrapped candies, confetti, or small toys through the flap;
21. Seal the flap closed with more paper-mache strips;
22. Allow to dry;
23. Decorate with paint, fringed paper or sparkles;
24. Hang and hit!!

More Multicultural Crafts

Beadwork Designs

Many beautiful designs are found in Native beadwork. Porcupine quills were dyed and sewn to leather bands or birch bark. Use the following activity to create designs that emulate this beadwork.

MATERIALS:

- Flat toothpicks
- Food colouring or jelly powder crystals (added to small quantities of water to create a dye bath for the toothpicks).
- Glue
- Strips of brown construction paper (bracelets)

WHAT TO DO:

1. Before beginning the activity, soak the toothpicks in food colouring or diluted jelly powder bath;
2. Allow toothpicks to dry;
3. After viewing examples of native beadwork, distribute strips of brown construction paper to be used as bracelets;
4. Model for the children how to create a design on their construction paper, by breaking the toothpicks to fit the design;
5. Next have children glue toothpick pieces making the design using colours of their choice;
6. The teacher may wish to read with the class several native stories and legends to act as inspiration for the children.

Teacher Tip: Lay toothpicks across the construction paper bracelets, so when bent they won't break.

Rangoli From India

Rangoli is an art technique learned by girls in some Indian homes. The art form is passed down from generation to generation. Decorating the floors with rice flour mixed with water is usually done for celebrations. The mixture is drizzled through the fingers to form intricate designs. The designs are temporary and wear off in a few days.

MATERIALS:

- Flour
- Water
- Tempera paint
- Wax paper
- Tubs to contain mixture

WHAT TO DO:

1. Before beginning this activity mix flour and water together to form a thin mixture;
2. Demonstrate for the children how to scoop a handful of flour and water out of the tub;
3. Drizzle the mixture onto a sheet of wax paper;
4. Leave undisturbed to dry;
5. Once dry, dip fingers into the tempera paint, and paint between the drizzles!

DISCUSSION:

How does your family prepare for celebrations or special events?

Japanese Carp Kites

Kite flying plays an important part in Japanese culture. **May 5** is the Boy's Festival. A carp kite is the symbol of courage, and is flown for every boy in a Japanese family. In this activity, stuffed carp can be flown over the classroom.

MATERIALS:
- Large tracers of fish
- Craft paper
- Paint
- Markers
- Newspaper
- Wool
- One-hole punch
- Optional: glue & sparkles

WHAT TO DO:
1. Have children trace a large carp fish shape onto a folded piece of craft paper;
2. Next have children cut out the fish shape;
3. Model for the children how to use the scissors to cut out scales;
4. Glue on scales and sprinkle with sparkles, or decorate with markers;
5. Demonstrate for the children how to hold the fish pieces together and staple the fish at the nose and tail;
6. Punch holes around the fish and have children "sew" the fish sides together, leaving an opening;
7. Remove staples and stuff the fish with newspaper;
8. Finish sewing the opening used to stuff the fish;
9. Display the stuffed fish by hanging them from the ceiling.

Tet Blossoms

The Vietnamese New Year is known as Tet, an abbreviation for "Tet Nguyen Dan" or first day. It is celebrated in late January or early February. Tet is a time when people try to catch up on things that they may not have done during the previous year. Bills are paid, borrowed items are returned, and all disagreements are forgiven and forgotten! Blossoms symbolize the rebirth, and welcome spring.

MATERIALS:
- Scissors
- Stapler
- Glue
- Brushes
- Magazines (optional)
- Small jar or bottle (baby food jars or juice bottles work well)
- Pipe cleaners or thin wire
- Tree branch
- Plaster of Paris
- Tissue paper cut into squares (about 10cm.)

WHAT TO DO:
1. Demonstrate for the children how to decorate the baby food jar or juice bottles by gluing pieces of magazine pictures on the outside of the jar;
2. Allow to dry;
3. While the bottle or jar is drying, stack 3 tissue paper squares on top of each other;
4. Fold the squares like a fan;
5. Staple the centre of the fan;
6. Round off the ends of the folded tissue paper;
7. Carefully pull the tissue paper layers apart;
8. Using the pipe cleaners or thin wire, attach the blossoms to the branch;
9. Mix the Plaster of Paris to a consistency of thick cream;
10. Have the children hold their branch in the jar or bottle while Plaster of Paris is poured into it;
11. Hold the branch in place until it is set in position;

Assessment Rubric

Outcome	Level 1	Level 2	Level 3	Level 4
Demonstrates an understanding that Canada is a country of many cultures	The student provided limited examples to show Canada may be made up of many cultures.	The student provided examples with some details to show Canada may be made up of many cultures.	The student provided considerable examples with many details to show Canada may be made up of many cultures.	The student provided comprehensive examples with extensive details to show Canada may be made up of many cultures.
Identifies community celebrations that reflect their heritage and Canadian identity	The student can identify few features of celebrations with limited detail. Provides basic information.	The student can identify features of celebrations with some detail. Provides clear information.	The student can identify many features of celebrations with considerable detail. Provides supporting information and is able to answer questions.	The student can identify comprehensive features of celebrations with high degree of detail. Provides supporting information and is able to answer questions with extensive explanations.
Describes family history and traditions made by individuals and groups in the local community	The student communicates about traditions and celebrations with limited understanding and few details.	The student communicates about traditions and celebrations with understanding and details.	The student communicates about traditions and celebrations with demonstrated understanding and good details.	The student communicates about traditions and celebrations with detailed understanding and accurate explanations.

Rubric for Student Self-Assessment

A	WOW	✓ I completed my work independently on time and with care. ✓ I added details and followed the instructions without help. ✓ I understand and can talk about what I have learned.
B	BRAVO	✓ I completed my work on time and with care. ✓ I followed the instructions with almost no help. ✓ I understand and can talk about what I have learned.
C	OKAY	✓ I completed my work. ✓ I followed the instructions with some help. ✓ I understand and can talk about most of what I have learned.
D	UH-OH	✓ I need to complete my work on time and with care. ✓ I should ask for help when I need it. ✓ I understand and can talk about a few of the things that I have learned.

GeoWat innovative teacher publishing ©2003